I want to be a sailor
Sailing on the sea,
I'd sail in a tugboat.
That would be fun for me.

I want to be a sailor
Sailing on the sea.
I'd sail in a sailing ship.
That would be fun for me.

I want to be a sailor
Sailing on the sea,
I'd sail in a fishing boat.
That would be fun for me.

I want to be a sailor
Sailing on the sea,
I'd sail in a containership.
That would be fun for me.

I want to be a sailor
Sailing on the sea,
I'd sail in a work boat.
That would be fun for me.

I want to be a sailor
Sailing on the sea,
I'd sail in a passenger ship.
That would be fun for me.

I want to be a sailor
Sailing on the sea,
I'd sail in a pilot boat.
That would be fun for me.

I want to be a sailor
Sailing on the sea,
I'd sail in a battleship.
That may **not** be fun for me